From the Heart Series - Old Tales for New Readers

The *From the Heart* series is inspired by Ancient Greek myths.
These stories have withstood the test of time and have a
power to engage people from different cultures and all age
groups. We have retold the stories in a modern setting. We
feel they will stimulate discussion and encourage students to
share their own stories.

Hazel is a writer and Myrna is an artist and storyteller. We met
when we were both teaching adult literacy at Kensington and
Chelsea College. We wanted our students to experience the
pleasure of reading books with really good stories.

Hazel Riley & Myrna Shoa

Elvis is inspired by the Greek myth of King Midas. Everything King Midas touched turned to gold. But this did not make him happy.

They called him the King.

It seemed that everything he touched

turned to gold.

He was a poor boy
from the wrong side of the tracks.

He became a superstar.

Gold records hung on his walls.

He had big gold rings on every finger

and heavy gold chains around his neck.

Gold Cadillacs filled his garage.

He even had a gold suit.

He had everything he'd ever dreamed of, and more.

But the King was not happy.

He was always hungry.

He ate more and more junk food.

He had hamburgers for breakfast, lunch and dinner.

Nothing satisfied him.

He drank too much.

He took drugs to help him sleep at night
and drugs to help him get up in the morning.

He lost his good looks.

His gold suit split at the seams.

He could only just squeeze into his gold Cadillac.

But he was still the King.

He still had the Midas touch.

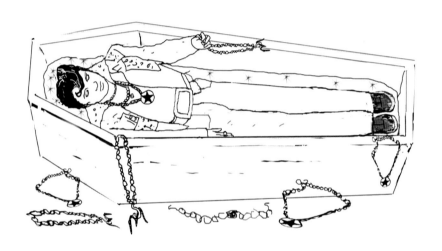

And when he died,

he was buried in a gold coffin.

The Midas Touch

King Midas was a kind man. When an old man was found in the garden, very drunk from partying with Dionysus, the God of Wine, Midas took him in. He gave the old man clean clothes and a soft bed to sleep in. The next day he ordered a feast and invited all his friends and family. The feast went on for ten days.

The God of Wine came to collect his old friend. He wanted to reward the king for his kindness. He said, "Make a wish and it will come true."

Midas had a lovely home and a happy family. People respected him. The country was at peace. What could he wish for? Then he had a brilliant idea.
"I wish that everything I touch turns to gold," he said.

He was really excited. With all the gold he could build new cities and temples to honour the Gods. There would be festivals and feasts every day. He couldn't wait to get started. He picked up an apple and it turned to gold. He picked up a jug of water and it turned to gold. He ran around the palace until he was hot, hungry and thirsty.
"Bring me food and a glass of wine," he shouted.

Servants hurried to bring his meal. He picked up a chicken leg, but before he could take a single bite, it turned to gold. He reached for a big bunch of grapes and longed for their cool, sweet juice, but before he tasted a single drop, they turned to gold. This went on for many days.

At last the God took pity on him.
"Go to the river and bathe in its waters," he said.

Midas did as he was told. The water washed away all the power of his magic touch. People say you can still find lumps of gold in this river today.